FIRST PAST THE POST® SERIES

11+ 3D Non-verbal Reasoning

BOOK 1

Topic Tests and Mixed Tests

How to use this pack to make the most of 11+ exam preparation

It is important to remember that for 11 plus exams there is no national syllabus, no pass mark and no retake option! It is therefore vitally important that your child is fully primed in order to perform to the best of their ability to give themselves the best possible chance on the day.

Unlike similar publications, the First Past the Post® series uniquely assesses your child's performance on a question-by-question basis, helping to identify areas for improvement and providing suggestions for further targeted tests.

3D Non-verbal Reasoning

This series of mini-tests is representative of the non-verbal reasoning section of contemporary multi-discipline 11+ tests, which typically have two papers and contains around a dozen such questions. The suggested time is provided based on classroom testing sessions held at our centre.

Never has it been more useful to learn from mistakes!

Students can improve by as much as 15 percent not only by focused practice but also by targeting any weak areas.

How to manage your child's own practice

To get the most up-to-date information log on to the ElevenPlusExams website (www.elevenplusexams.co.uk). ElevenPlusExams is the largest UK on-line resource with over 40,000 webpages and a forum administered by a select group of experienced moderators.

About the authors

The ElevenPlusExams **First Past the Post®** series has been created by a team of experienced tutors and authors from leading British universities including Oxford and Cambridge.

Published by University of Buckingham Press

With special thanks to all the children who tested our material at the ElevenPlusExams centre in Harrow.

ISBN: 9781908684318

Copyright © ElevenPlusExams.co.uk 2013

Contents Page

This workbook is comprised of 8 tests. The first four are specific to each style of 3D NVR, made up of 24 questions and each should take 12 minutes to complete. The final four tests are mixed papers including all 4 styles of 3D NVR, made up of 21 questions and each should take 11 minutes to complete.

Once you have completed each test, using the answers, mark the tests and upload them onto our 11+ Peer Compare System™ to see how well you performed in comparison to others who have taken this test.

You can register by visiting www.ElevenPlusExams.co.uk/FirstPastThePost to post your results anonymously and obtain the feedback.

BLANK PAGE

FIRST PAST THE POST® SERIES

3D Non-verbal Reasoning

Paper 1 - 3D Views

Page	2	3	4	5	Total
Mark	/6	/6	/6	/6	/24

Read the following instructions carefully:

1. You have **12 minutes** to complete this test of **24 questions**.

2. Work as quickly and carefully as you can.

3. When you have finished a page, go straight onto the next page until you finish the test.

4. To change an answer, rub out your original answer and mark your new answer clearly.

5. If you are unsure of the answer then choose the one you think is most appropriate or return to it later.

6. When you have completed this paper go back to any questions you have missed out and check your answers.

Good luck!

After you have finished this paper you can use the 11+ Peer Compare System™ to see how well you performed compared to others who have taken this test. You can register by visiting www.ElevenPlusExams.co.uk/FirstPastThePost to post your results anonymously and obtain the feedback.

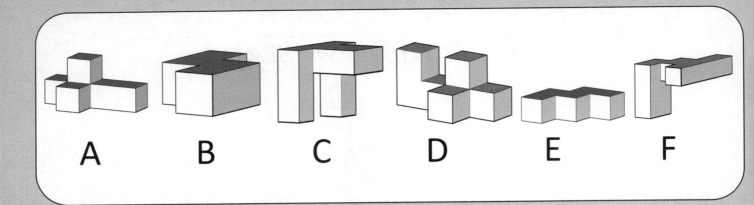

A   B   C   D   E   F

3D Views

The shape in the box on the left may be a rotation of one of the shapes shown above. Identify the shape by the letter or mark 'None'.

1.

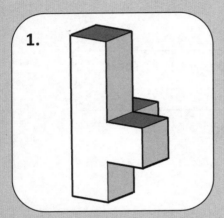

A ☐   D ☐

B ☐   E ☐

C ☐   F ☐

None ☐

2.

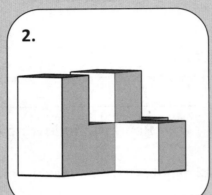

A ☐   D ☐

B ☐   E ☐

C ☐   F ☐

None ☐

3.

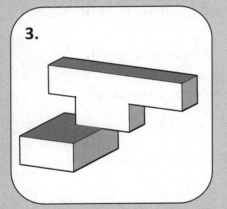

A ☐   D ☐

B ☐   E ☐

C ☐   F ☐

None ☐

4.

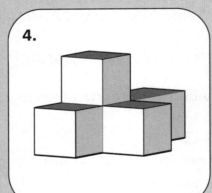

A ☐   D ☐

B ☐   E ☐

C ☐   F ☐

None ☐

5.

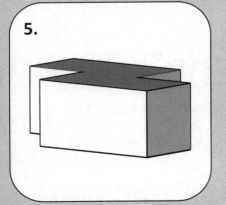

A ☐   D ☐

B ☐   E ☐

C ☐   F ☐

None ☐

6.

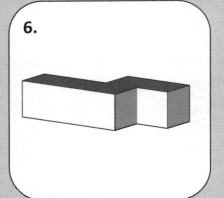

A ☐   D ☐

B ☐   E ☐

C ☐   F ☐

None ☐

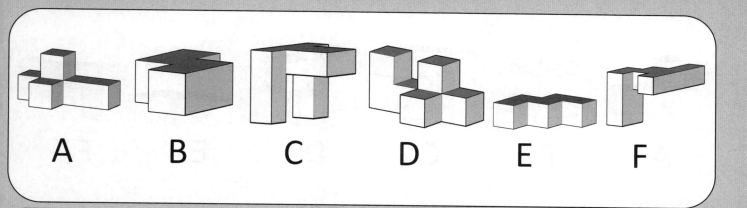

| A | B | C | D | E | F |

3D Views

The shape in the box on the left may be a rotation of one of the shapes shown above. Identify the shape by the letter or mark 'None'.

7.

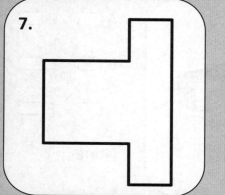

A ☐   D ☐

B ☐   E ☐

C ☐   F ☐

None ☐

8.

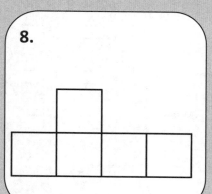

A ☐   D ☐

B ☐   E ☐

C ☐   F ☐

None ☐

9.

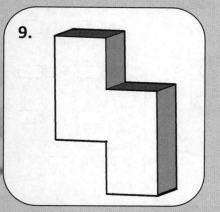

A ☐   D ☐

B ☐   E ☐

C ☐   F ☐

None ☐

10.

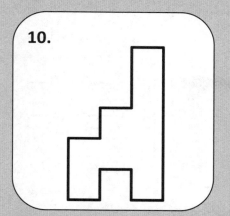

A ☐   D ☐

B ☐   E ☐

C ☐   F ☐

None ☐

11.

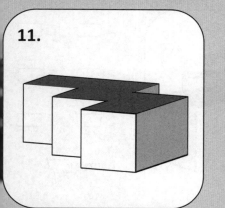

A ☐   D ☐

B ☐   E ☐

C ☐   F ☐

None ☐

12.

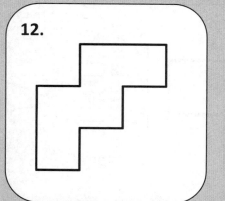

A ☐   D ☐

B ☐   E ☐

C ☐   F ☐

None ☐

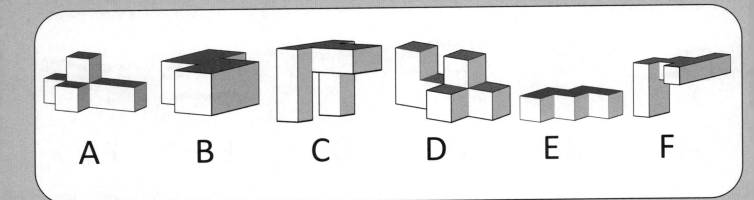

A   B   C   D   E   F

3D Views

The shape in the box on the left may be a rotation of one of the shapes shown above. Identify the shape by the letter or mark 'None'.

13.

A ☐   D ☐

B ☐   E ☐

C ☐   F ☐

None ☐

14.

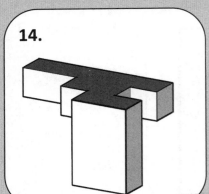

A ☐   D ☐

B ☐   E ☐

C ☐   F ☐

None ☐

15.

A ☐   D ☐

B ☐   E ☐

C ☐   F ☐

None ☐

16.

A ☐   D ☐

B ☐   E ☐

C ☐   F ☐

None ☐

17.

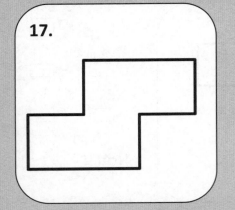

A ☐   D ☐

B ☐   E ☐

C ☐   F ☐

None ☐

18.

A ☐   D ☐

B ☐   E ☐

C ☐   F ☐

None ☐

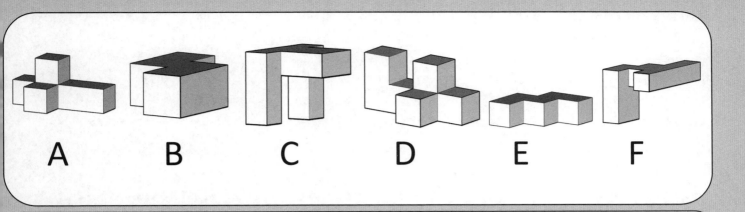

3D Views

The shape in the box on the left may be a rotation of one of the shapes shown above. Identify the shape by the letter or mark 'None'.

19.

A ☐   D ☐

B ☐   E ☐

C ☐   F ☐

None ☐

20.

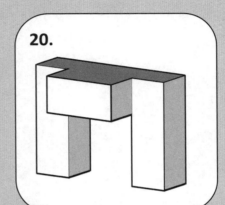

A ☐   D ☐

B ☐   E ☐

C ☐   F ☐

None ☐

21.

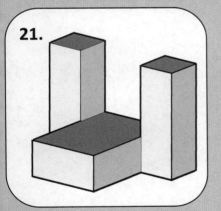

A ☐   D ☐

B ☐   E ☐

C ☐   F ☐

None ☐

22.

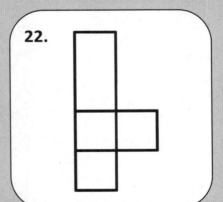

A ☐   D ☐

B ☐   E ☐

C ☐   F ☐

None ☐

23.

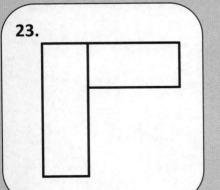

A ☐   D ☐

B ☐   E ☐

C ☐   F ☐

None ☐

24.

A ☐   D ☐

B ☐   E ☐

C ☐   F ☐

None ☐

FIRST PAST THE POST® SERIES

3D Non-verbal Reasoning
Paper 2 - 3D Composite Shapes

Page	8	9	10	11	12	Total
Mark	/5	/5	/5	/5	/4	/24

Read the following instructions carefully:

1. You have **12 minutes** to complete this test of **24 questions**.

2. Work as quickly and carefully as you can.

3. When you have finished a page, go straight onto the next page until you finish the test.

4. To change an answer, rub out your original answer and mark your new answer clearly.

5. If you are unsure of the answer then choose the one you think is most appropriate or return to it later.

6. When you have completed this paper go back to any questions you have missed out and check your answers.

Good luck!

After you have finished this paper you can use the 11+ Peer Compare System™ to see how well you performed compared to others who have taken this test. You can register by visiting www.ElevenPlusExams.co.uk/FirstPastThePost to post your results anonymously and obtain the feedback.

3D Composite Shapes

Work out which set of blocks can be put together to make the 3D figure on the left.

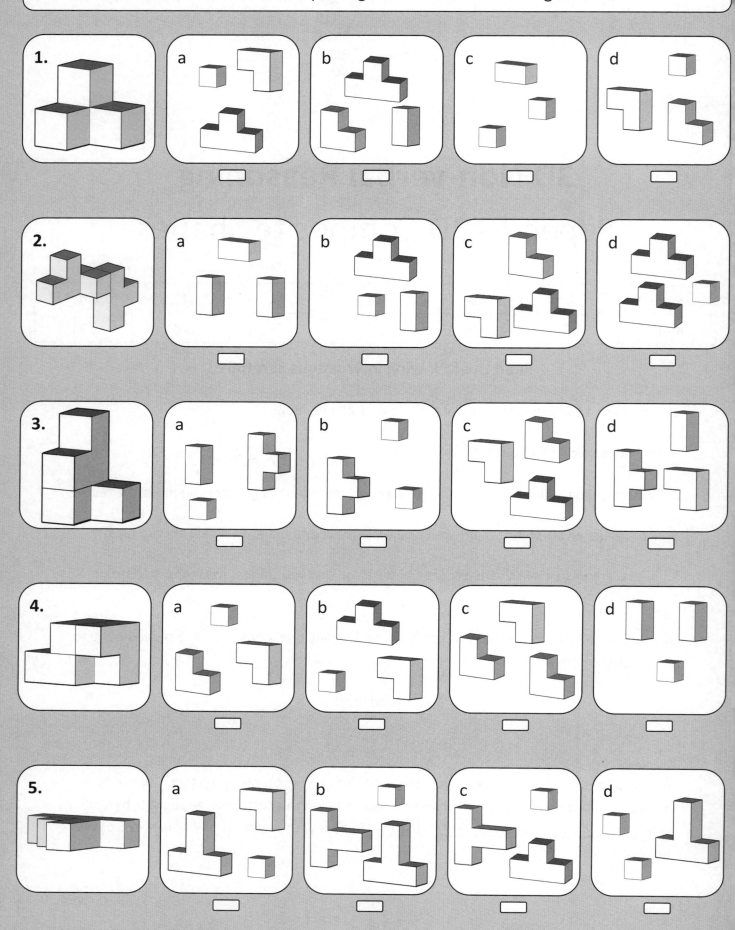

3D Composite Shapes

Work out which set of blocks can be put together to make the 3D figure on the left.

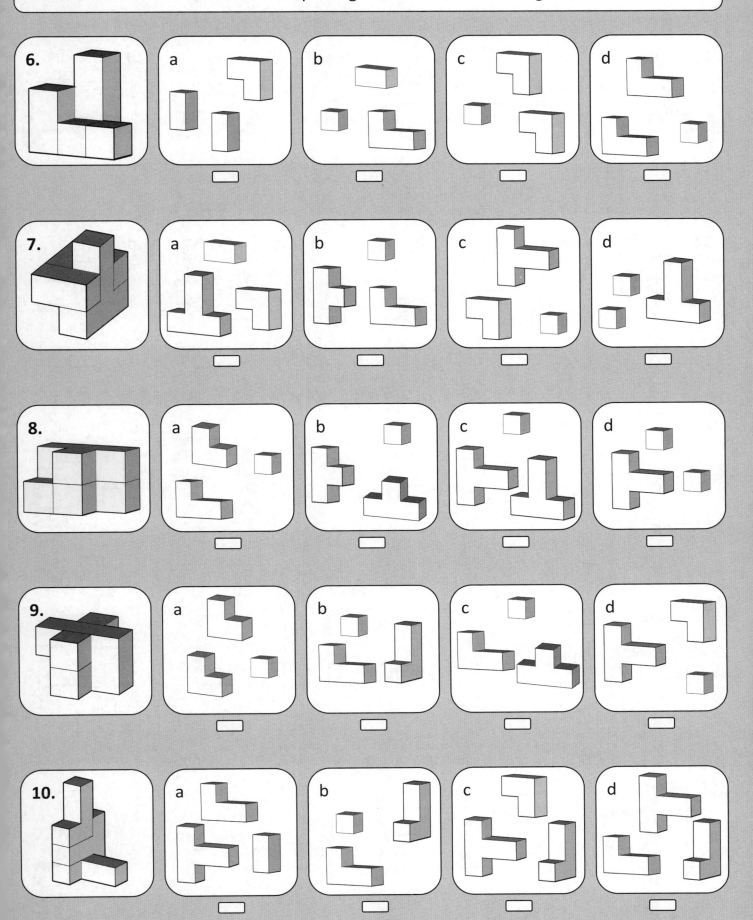

3D Composite Shapes

Work out which set of blocks can be put together to make the 3D figure on the left.

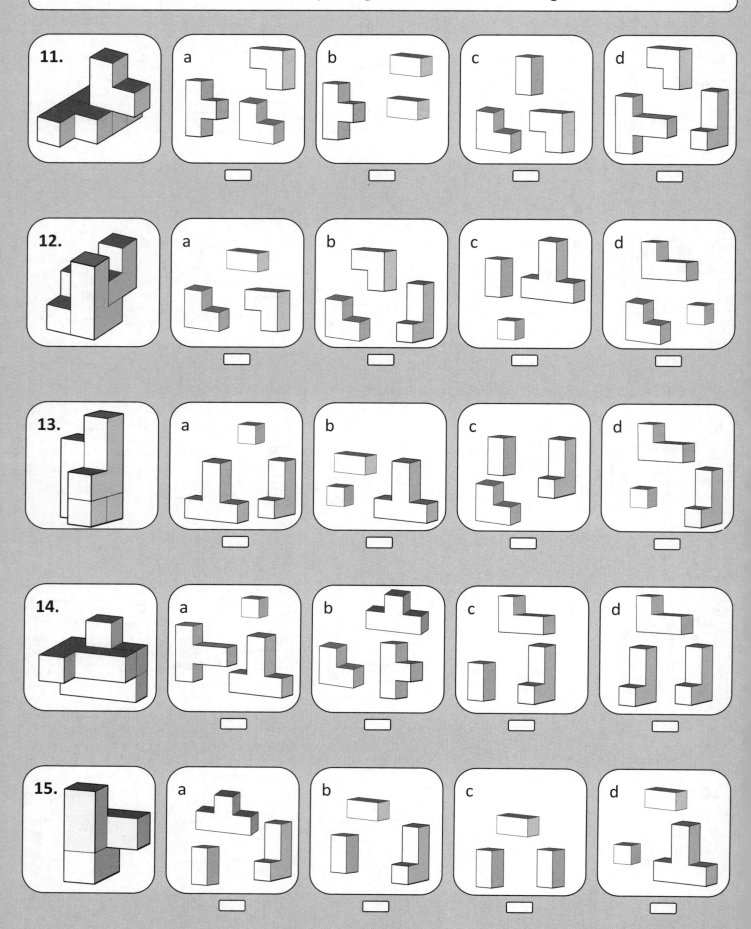

3D Composite Shapes

Work out which set of blocks can be put together to make the 3D figure on the left.

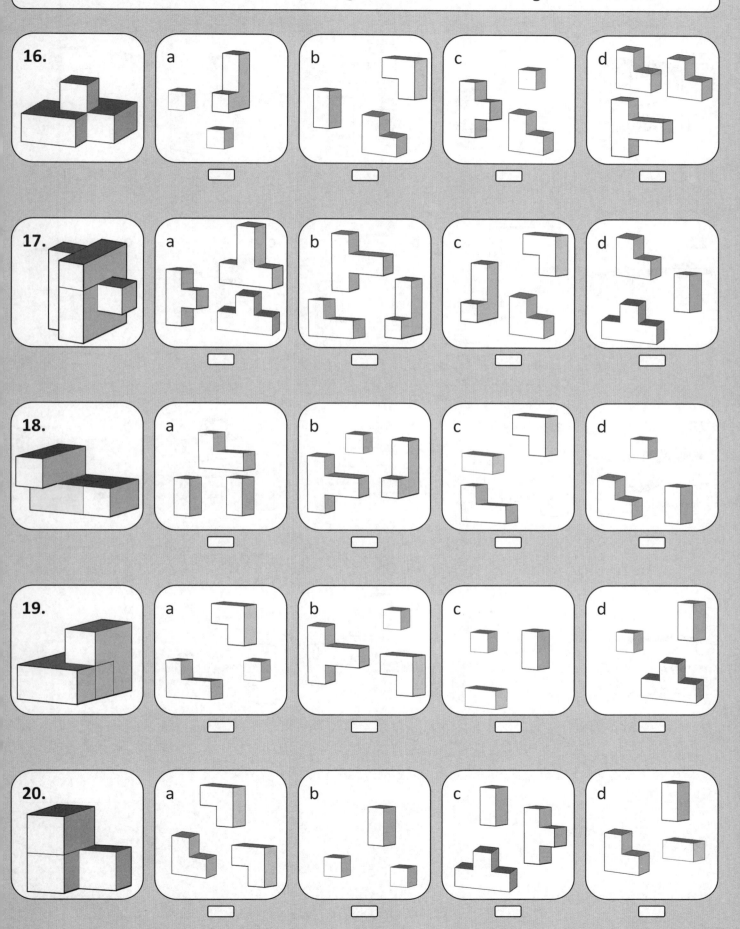

3D Composite Shapes

Work out which set of blocks can be put together to make the 3D figure on the left.

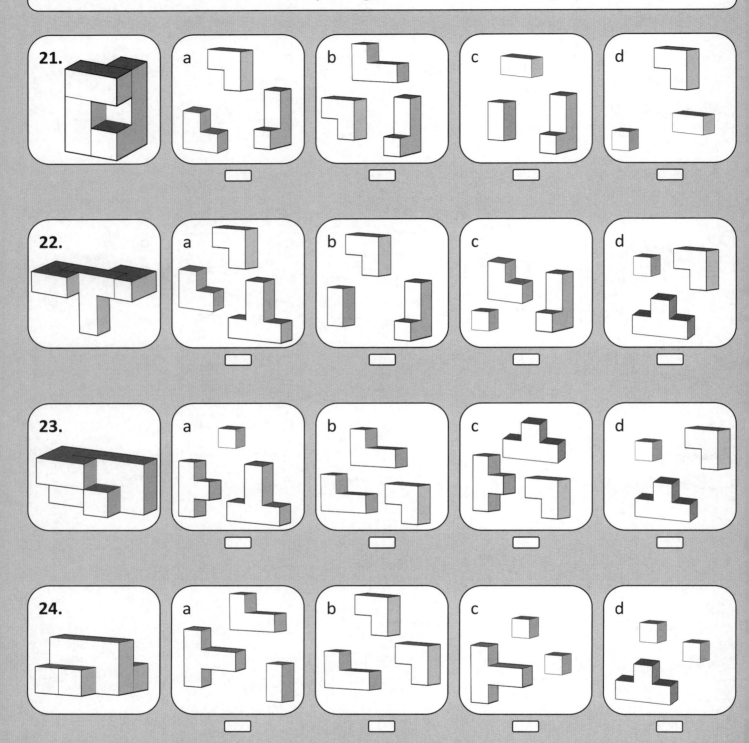

21.   a   b   c   d

22.   a   b   c   d

23.   a   b   c   d

24.   a   b   c   d

3D Non-verbal Reasoning

Paper 3 - 3D Cube Nets

Page	14	15	16	17	18	Total
Mark	/5	/5	/5	/5	/4	/24

Read the following instructions carefully:

1. You have **12 minutes** to complete this test of **24 questions**.

2. Work as quickly and carefully as you can.

3. When you have finished a page, go straight onto the next page until you finish the test.

4. To change an answer, rub out your original answer and mark your new answer clearly.

5. If you are unsure of the answer then choose the one you think is most appropriate or return to it later.

6. When you have completed this paper go back to any questions you have missed out and check your answers.

Good luck!

After you have finished this paper you can use the 11+ Peer Compare System™ to see how well you performed compared to others who have taken this test. You can register by visiting www.ElevenPlusExams.co.uk/FirstPastThePost to post your results anonymously and obtain the feedback.

3D Cube Nets

Work out which of the four cubes can be made from the net.

6.
    a
    b
    c
    d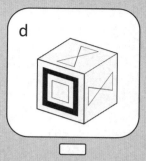

7.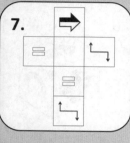
    a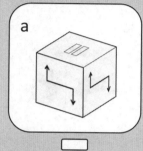
    b
    c
    d

8.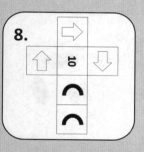
    a
    b
    c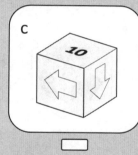
    d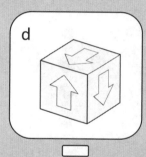

9.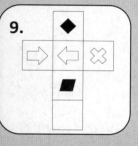
    a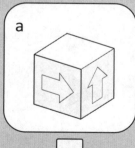
    b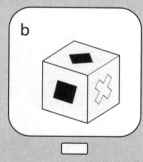
    c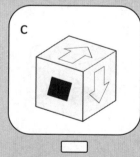
    d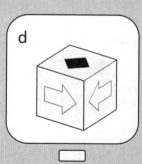

10.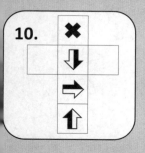
    a
    b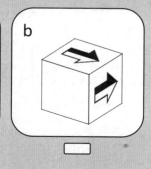
    c
    d

3D Cube Nets

Work out which of the four cubes can be made from the net.

11.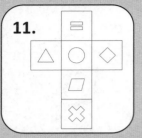

a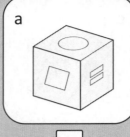

b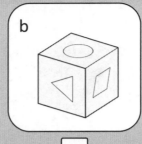

c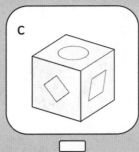

d

12.

a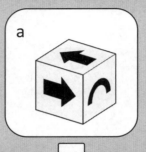

b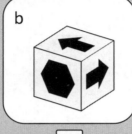

c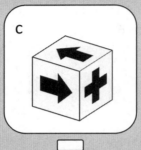

d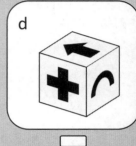

13.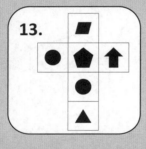

a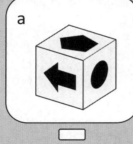

b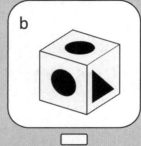

c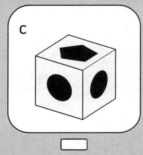

d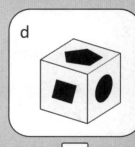

14.

a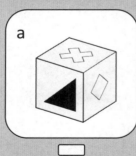

b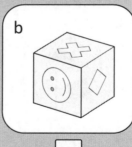

c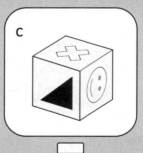

d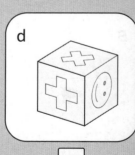

15.

a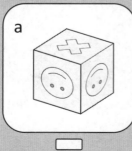

b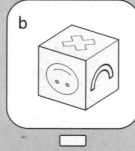

c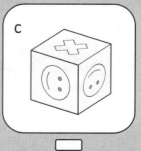

d

3D Cube Nets

Work out which of the four cubes can be made from the net.

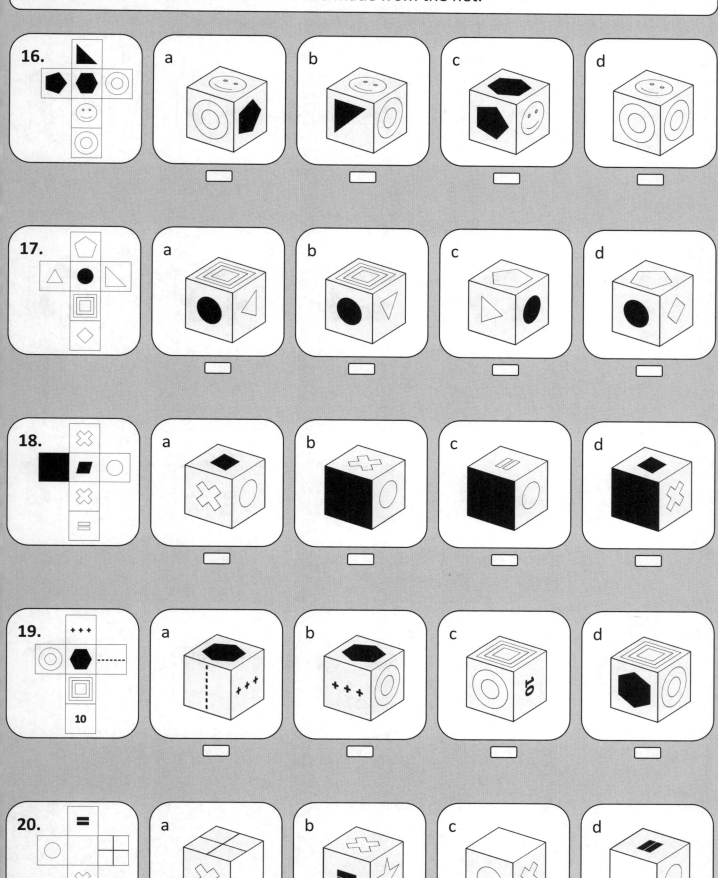

16. a   b   c   d

17. a   b   c   d

18. a   b   c   d

19. a   b   c   d

20. a   b   c   d

3D Cube Nets

Work out which of the four cubes can be made from the net.

21. 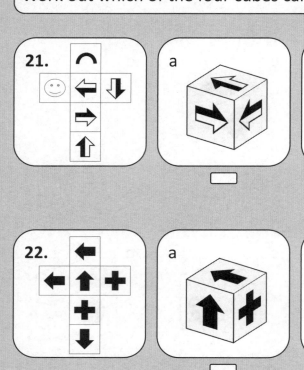 a 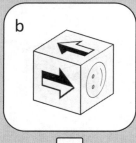 b  c  d

22. 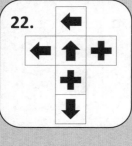 a 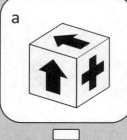 b 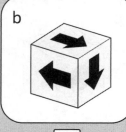 c 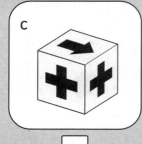 d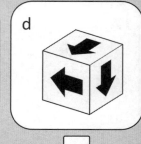

23. 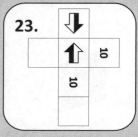 a 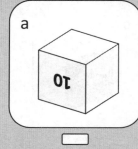 b 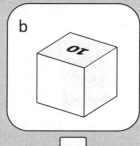 c 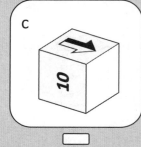 d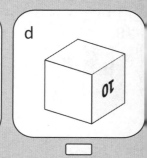

24. 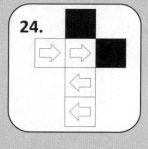 a 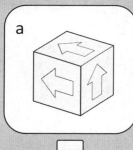 b  c 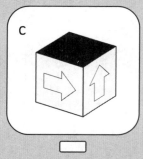 d

FIRST PAST THE POST® SERIES

3D Non-verbal Reasoning
Paper 4 - 3D Plan Views

Page	20	21	22	23	24	Total
Mark	/5	/5	/5	/5	/4	/24

Read the following instructions carefully:

1. You have **12 minutes** to complete this test of **24 questions**.

2. Work as quickly and carefully as you can.

3. When you have finished a page, go straight onto the next page until you finish the test.

4. To change an answer, rub out your original answer and mark your new answer clearly.

5. If you are unsure of the answer then choose the one you think is most appropriate or return to it later.

6. When you have completed this paper go back to any questions you have missed out and check your answers.

Good luck!

After you have finished this paper you can use the <u>11+ Peer Compare System</u>™ to see how well you performed compared to others who have taken this test. You can register by visiting <u>www.ElevenPlusExams.co.uk/FirstPastThePost</u> to post your results anonymously and obtain the feedback.

3D Plan Views

Work out which option is a birds eye view (plan view) of the 3D figure on the left.

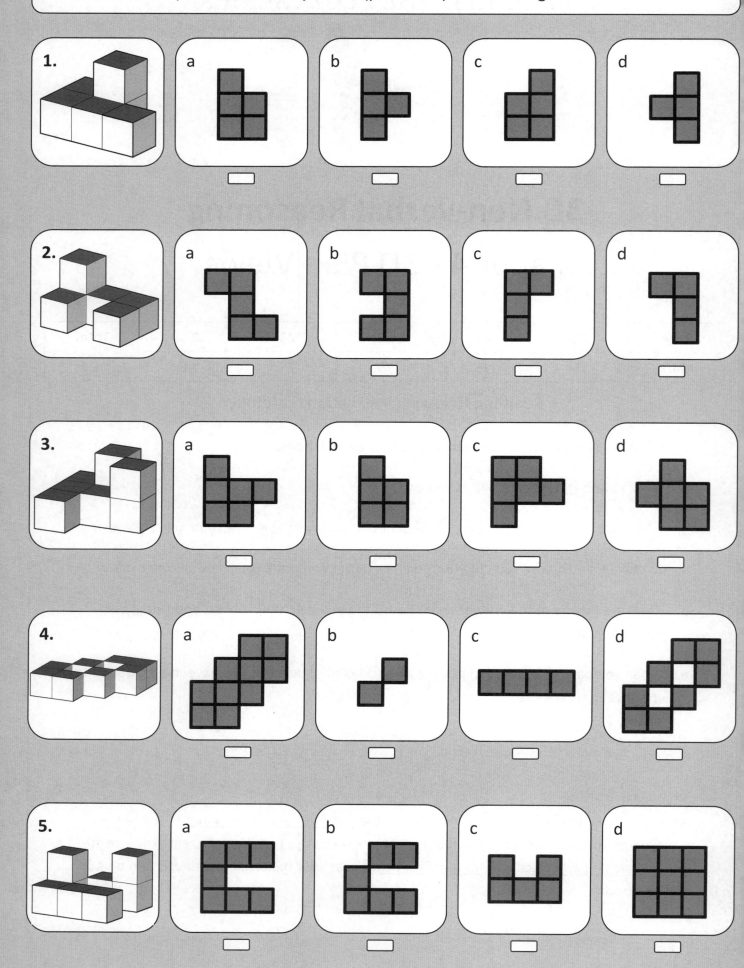

1. a b c d

2. a b c d

3. a b c d

4. a b c d

5. a b c d

3D Plan Views

Work out which option is a birds eye view (plan view) of the 3D figure on the left.

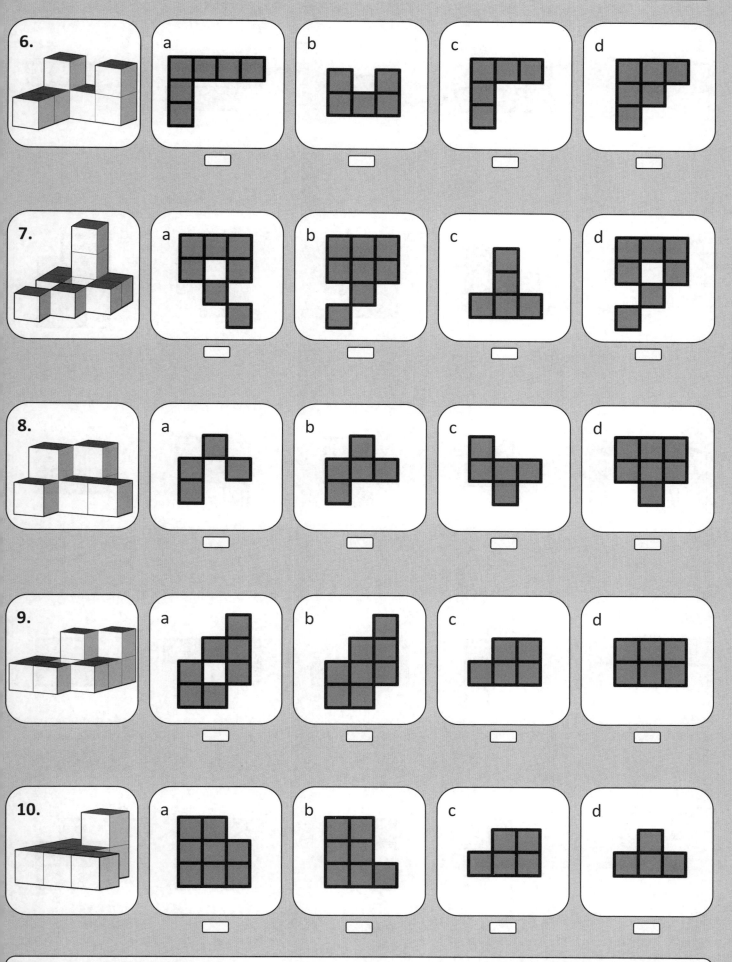

6.   a   b   c   d

7.   a   b   c   d

8.   a   b   c   d

9.   a   b   c   d

10.   a   b   c   d

3D Plan Views

Work out which option is a birds eye view (plan view) of the 3D figure on the left.

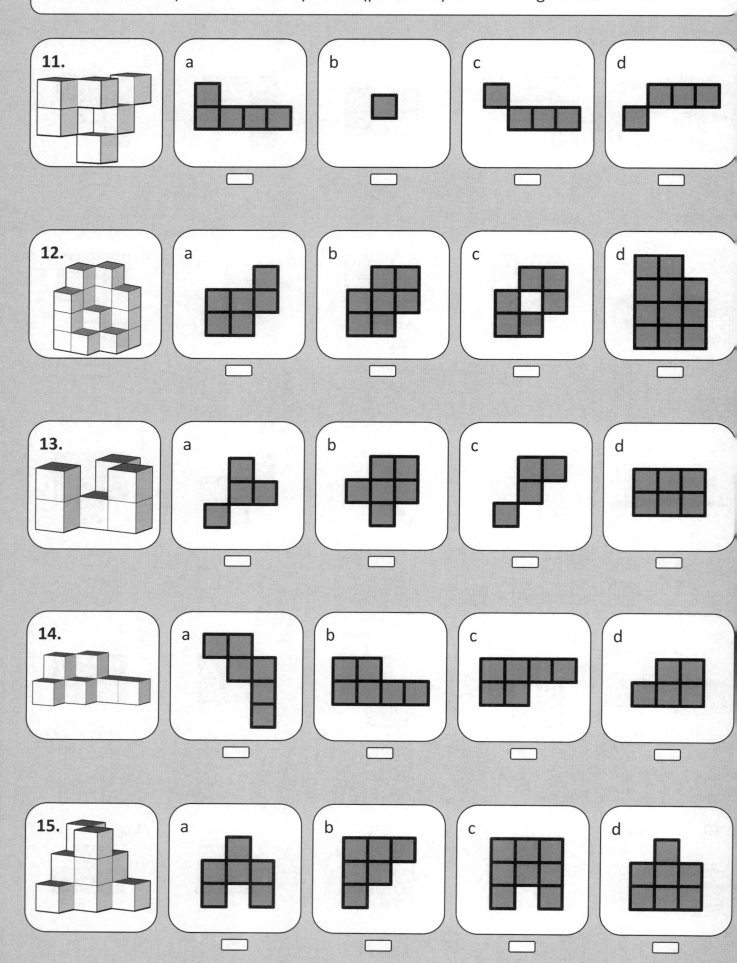

3D Plan Views

Work out which option is a birds eye view (plan view) of the 3D figure on the left.

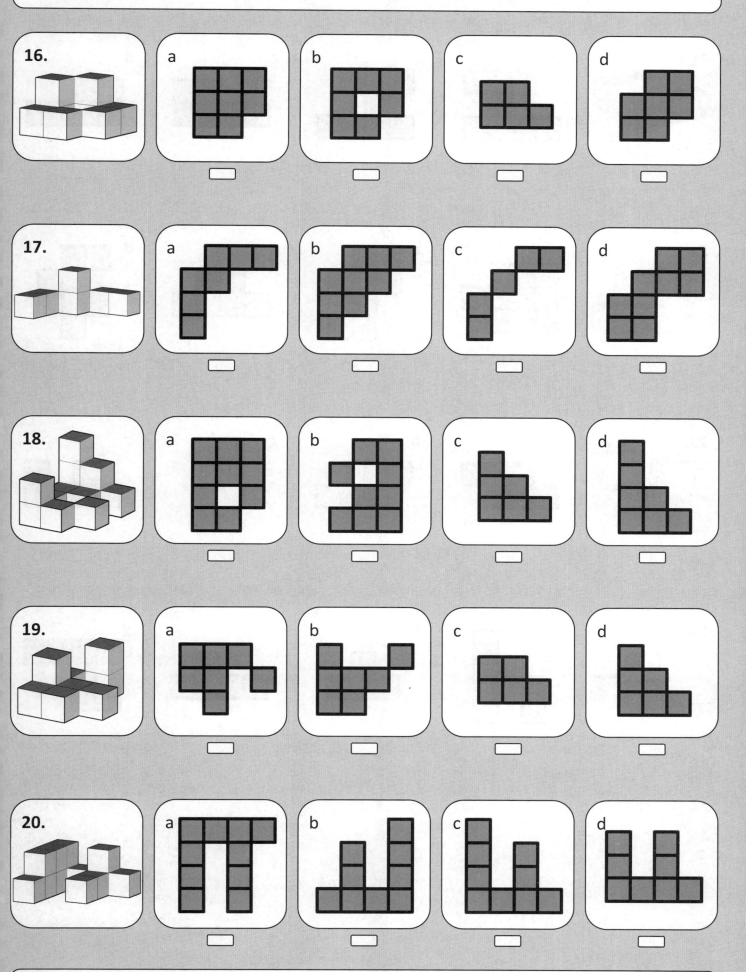

3D Plan Views

Work out which option is a birds eye view (plan view) of the 3D figure on the left.

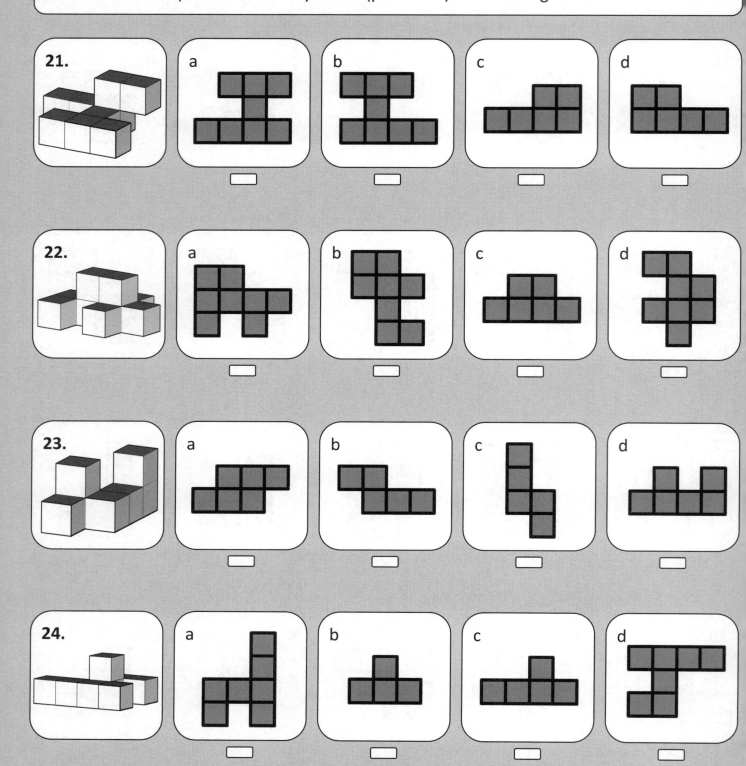

21. a b c d

22. a b c d

23. a b c d

24. a b c d

FIRST PAST THE POST® SERIES

3D Non-verbal Reasoning

Mixed Paper 1

Page	26	27	28	29	Total
Mark	/6	/5	/5	/5	/21

Read the following instructions carefully:

1. You have **11 minutes** to complete this test of **21 questions**.

2. Work as quickly and carefully as you can.

3. When you have finished a page, go straight onto the next page until you finish the test.

4. To change an answer, rub out your original answer and mark your new answer clearly.

5. If you are unsure of the answer then choose the one you think is most appropriate or return to it later.

6. When you have completed this paper go back to any questions you have missed out and check your answers.

Good luck!

After you have finished this paper you can use the <u>11+ Peer Compare System</u>™ to see how well you performed compared to others who have taken this test. You can register by visiting <u>www.ElevenPlusExams.co.uk/FirstPastThePost</u> to post your results anonymously and obtain the feedback.

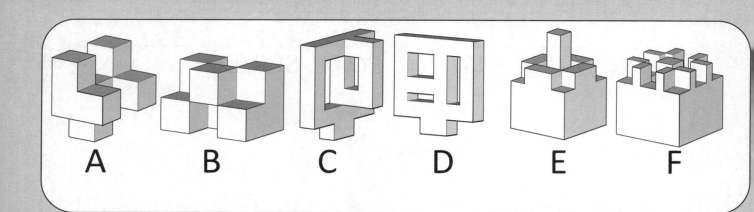

3D Views

The shape in the box on the left may be a rotation of one of the shapes shown above. Identify the shape by the letter or mark 'None'.

1.

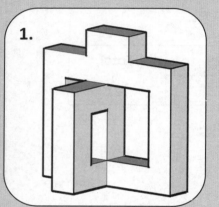

A ☐   D ☐

B ☐   E ☐

C ☐   F ☐

None ☐

2.

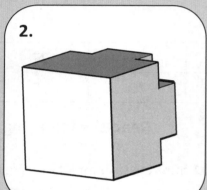

A ☐   D ☐

B ☐   E ☐

C ☐   F ☐

None ☐

3.

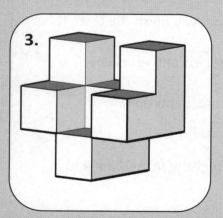

A ☐   D ☐

B ☐   E ☐

C ☐   F ☐

None ☐

4.

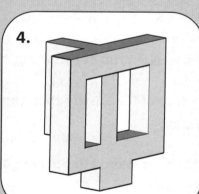

A ☐   D ☐

B ☐   E ☐

C ☐   F ☐

None ☐

5.

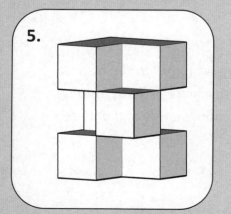

A ☐   D ☐

B ☐   E ☐

C ☐   F ☐

None ☐

6.

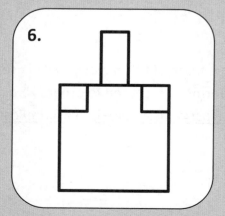

A ☐   D ☐

B ☐   E ☐

C ☐   F ☐

None ☐

3D Composite Shapes

Work out which set of blocks can be put together to make the 3D figure on the left.

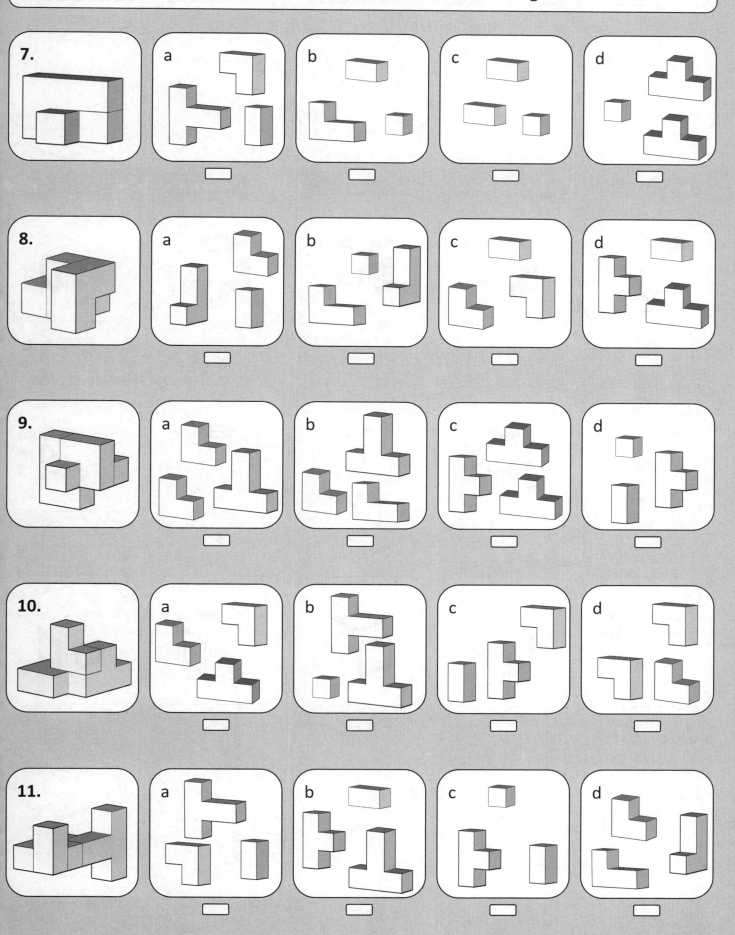

3D Cube Nets

Work out which of the four cubes can be made from the net.

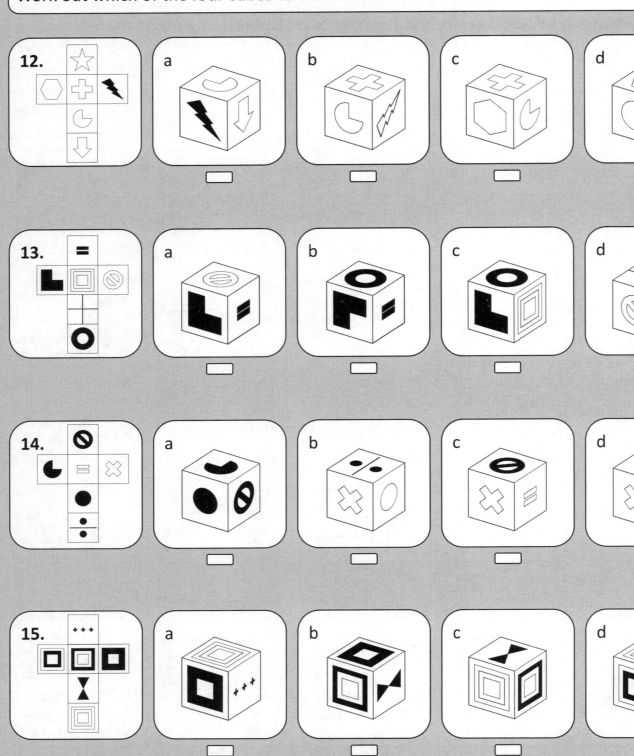

3D Plan Views

Work out which option is a birds eye view (plan view) of the 3D figure on the left.

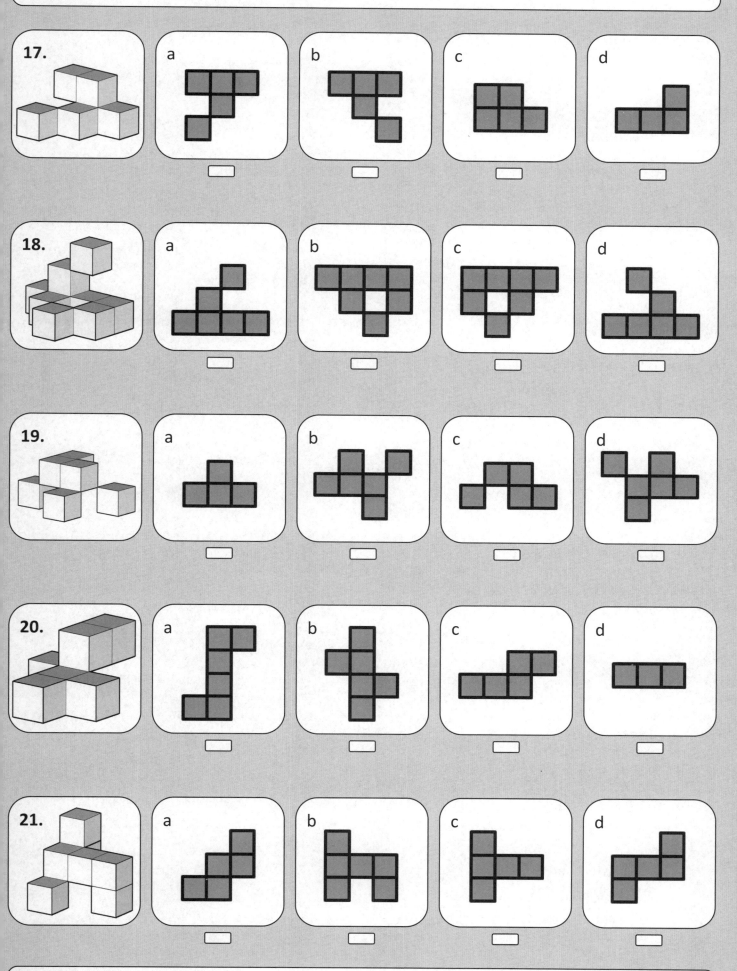

BLANK PAGE

FIRST PAST THE POST® SERIES

3D Non-verbal Reasoning

Mixed Paper 2

Page	32	33	34	35	Total
Mark	/6	/5	/5	/5	/21

Read the following instructions carefully:

1. You have **11 minutes** to complete this test of **21 questions**.

2. Work as quickly and carefully as you can.

3. When you have finished a page, go straight onto the next page until you finish the test.

4. To change an answer, rub out your original answer and mark your new answer clearly.

5. If you are unsure of the answer then choose the one you think is most appropriate or return to it later.

6. When you have completed this paper go back to any questions you have missed out and check your answers.

Good luck!

After you have finished this paper you can use the 11+ Peer Compare System™ to see how well you performed compared to others who have taken this test. You can register by visiting www.ElevenPlusExams.co.uk/FirstPastThePost to post your results anonymously and obtain the feedback.

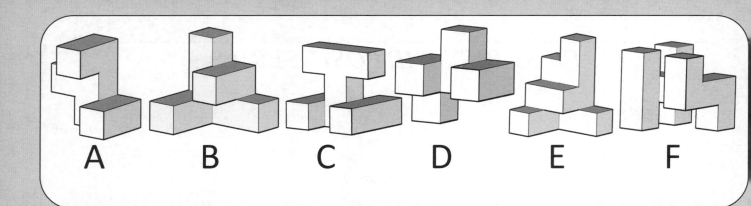

3D Views

The shape in the box on the left may be a rotation of one of the shapes shown above. Identify the shape by the letter or mark 'None'.

1.

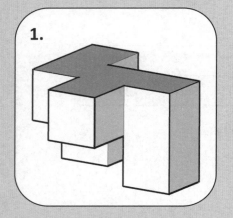

A ☐   D ☐

B ☐   E ☐

C ☐   F ☐

None ☐

2.

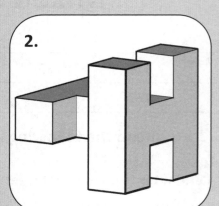

A ☐   D ☐

B ☐   E ☐

C ☐   F ☐

None ☐

3.

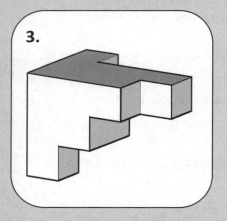

A ☐   D ☐

B ☐   E ☐

C ☐   F ☐

None ☐

4.

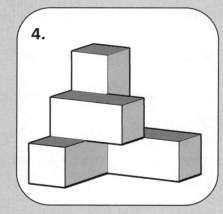

A ☐   D ☐

B ☐   E ☐

C ☐   F ☐

None ☐

5.

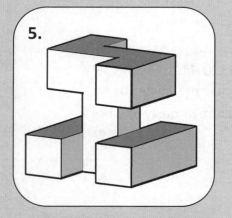

A ☐   D ☐

B ☐   E ☐

C ☐   F ☐

None ☐

6.

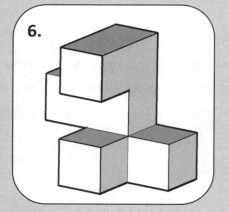

A ☐   D ☐

B ☐   E ☐

C ☐   F ☐

None ☐

3D Composite Shapes

Work out which set of blocks can be put together to make the 3D figure on the left.

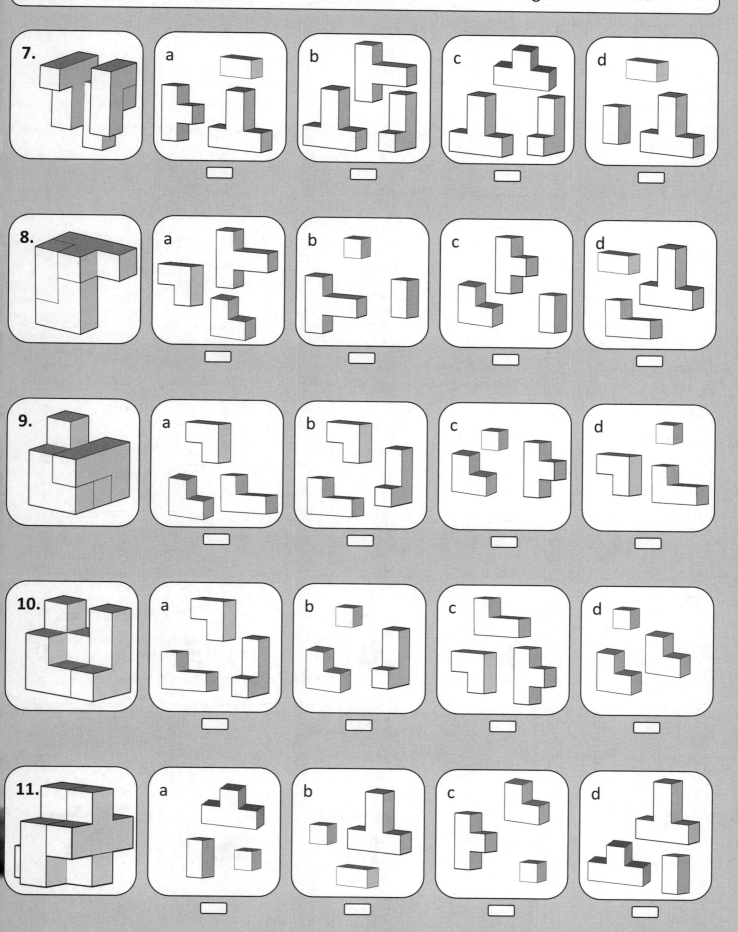

3D Cube Nets

Work out which of the four cubes can be made from the net.

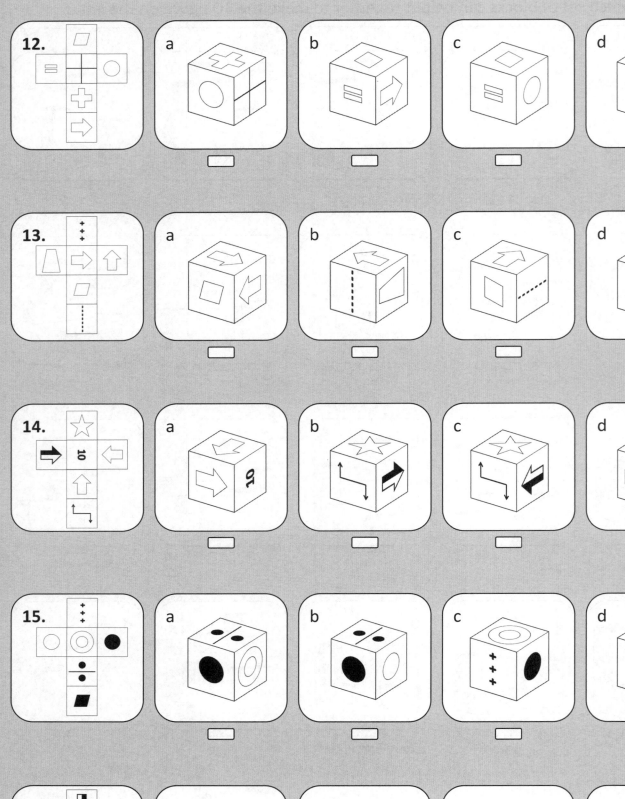

3D Plan Views

Work out which option is a birds eye view (plan view) of the 3D figure on the left.

BLANK PAGE

FIRST PAST THE POST® SERIES

3D Non-verbal Reasoning
Mixed Paper 3

Page	38	39	40	41	Total
Mark	/6	/5	/5	/5	/21

Read the following instructions carefully:

1. You have **11 minutes** to complete this test of **21 questions**.

2. Work as quickly and carefully as you can.

3. When you have finished a page, go straight onto the next page until you finish the test.

4. To change an answer, rub out your original answer and mark your new answer clearly.

5. If you are unsure of the answer then choose the one you think is most appropriate or return to it later.

6. When you have completed this paper go back to any questions you have missed out and check your answers.

Good luck!

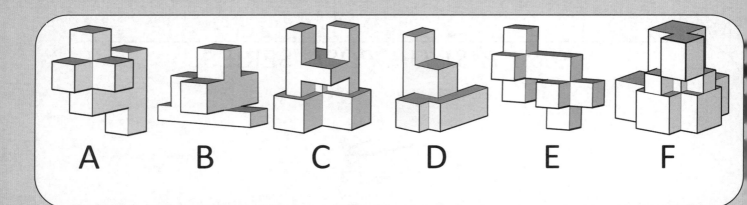

A   B   C   D   E   F

3D Views

The shape in the box on the left may be a rotation of one of the shapes shown above. Identify the shape by the letter or mark 'None'.

1.

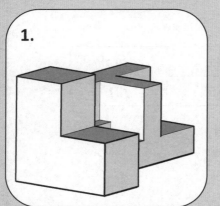

A ☐   D ☐

B ☐   E ☐

C ☐   F ☐

None ☐

2.

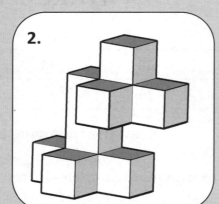

A ☐   D ☐

B ☐   E ☐

C ☐   F ☐

None ☐

3.

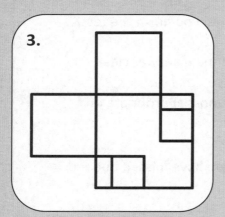

A ☐   D ☐

B ☐   E ☐

C ☐   F ☐

None ☐

4.

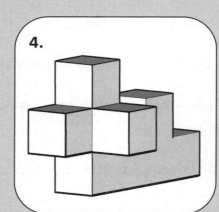

A ☐   D ☐

B ☐   E ☐

C ☐   F ☐

None ☐

5.

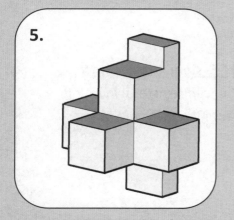

A ☐   D ☐

B ☐   E ☐

C ☐   F ☐

None ☐

6.

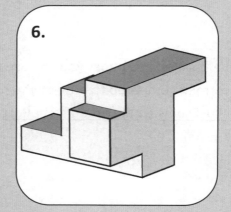

A ☐   D ☐

B ☐   E ☐

C ☐   F ☐

None ☐

3D Composite Shapes

Work out which set of blocks can be put together to make the 3D figure on the left.

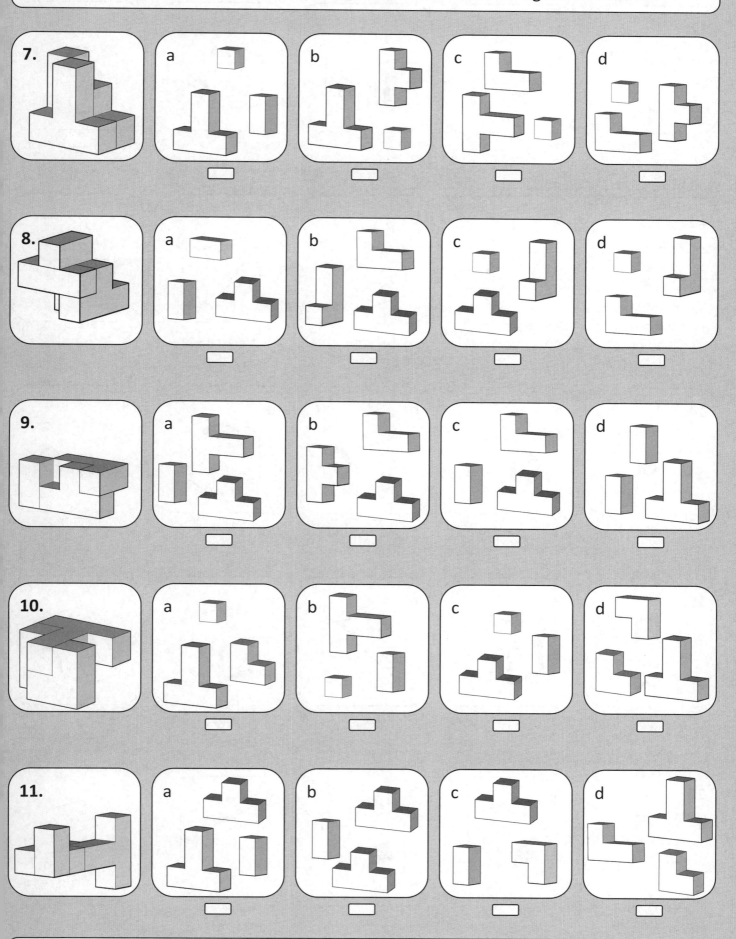

3D Cube Nets

Work out which of the four cubes can be made from the net.

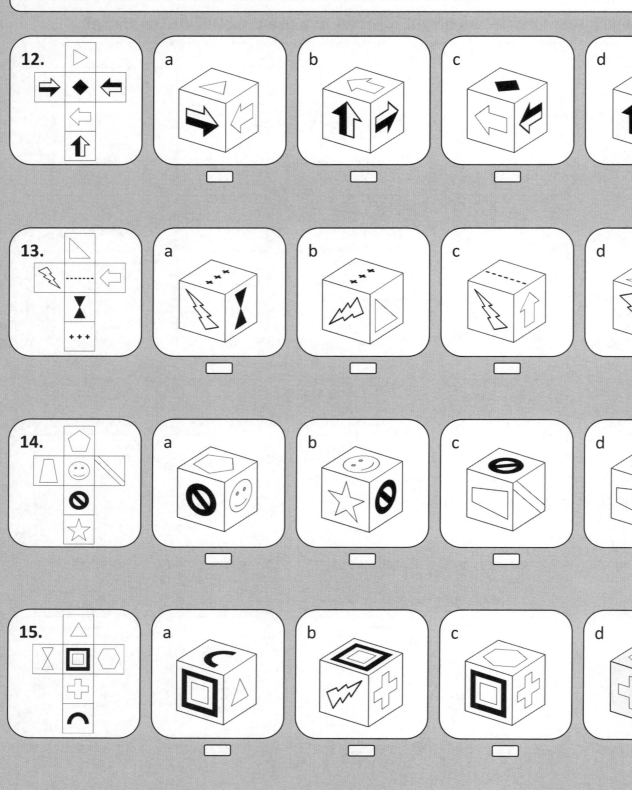

12. | a | b | c | d

13. | a | b | c | d

14. | a | b | c | d

15. | a | b | c | d

16. | a | b | c | d

 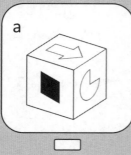 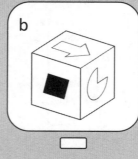 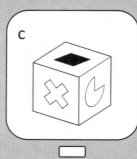 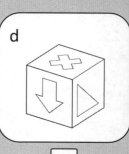

3D Plan Views

Work out which option is a birds eye view (plan view) of the 3D figure on the left.

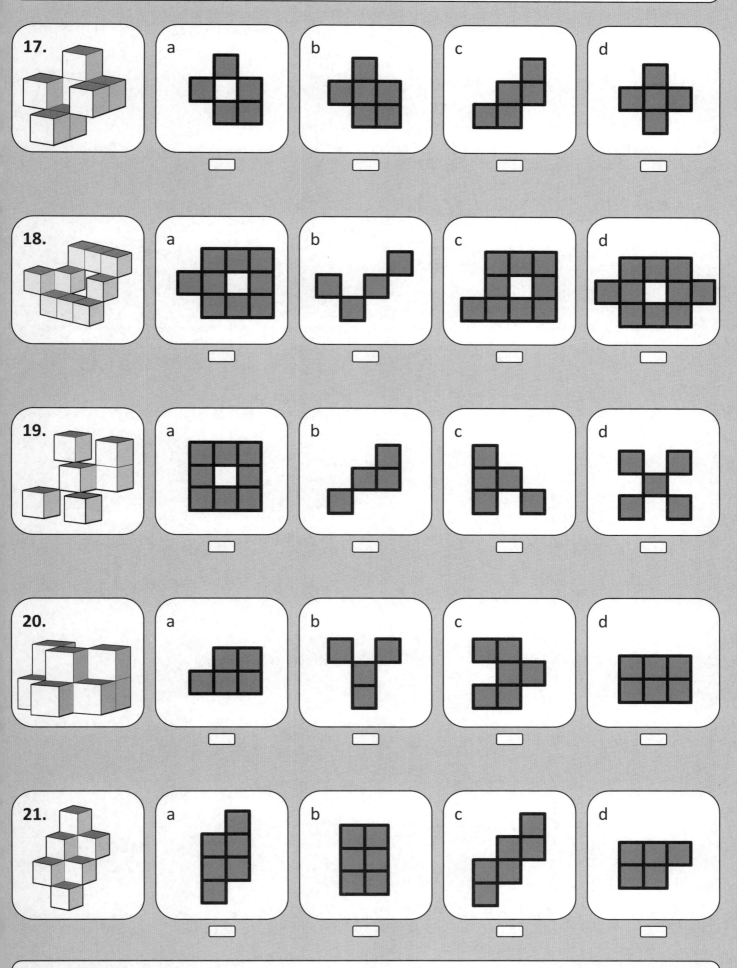

BLANK PAGE

FIRST PAST THE POST® SERIES

3D Non-verbal Reasoning

Mixed Paper 4

Page	44	45	46	47	Total
Mark	/6	/5	/5	/5	/21

Read the following instructions carefully:

1. You have **11 minutes** to complete this test of **21 questions**.

2. Work as quickly and carefully as you can.

3. When you have finished a page, go straight onto the next page until you finish the test.

4. To change an answer, rub out your original answer and mark your new answer clearly.

5. If you are unsure of the answer then choose the one you think is most appropriate or return to it later.

6. When you have completed this paper go back to any questions you have missed out and check your answers.

Good luck!

After you have finished this paper you can use the 11+ Peer Compare System™ to see how well you performed compared to others who have taken this test. You can register by visiting www.ElevenPlusExams.co.uk/FirstPastThePost to post your results anonymously and obtain the feedback.

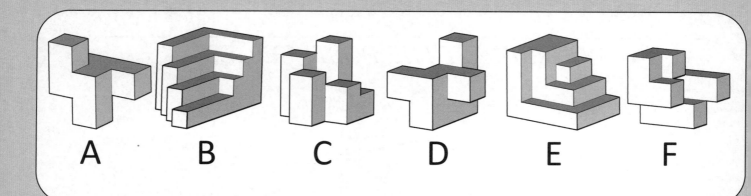

3D Views

The shape in the box on the left may be a rotation of one of the shapes shown above. Identify the shape by the letter or mark 'None'.

1.

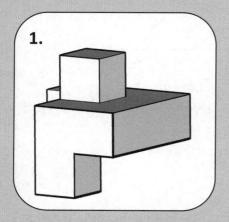

A ▢ D ▢

B ▢ E ▢

C ▢ F ▢

None ▢

2.

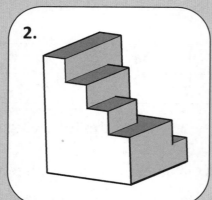

A ▢ D ▢

B ▢ E ▢

C ▢ F ▢

None ▢

3.

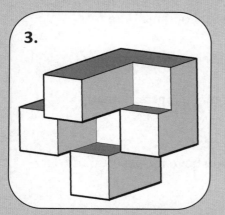

A ▢ D ▢

B ▢ E ▢

C ▢ F ▢

None ▢

4.

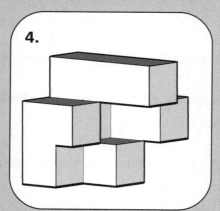

A ▢ D ▢

B ▢ E ▢

C ▢ F ▢

None ▢

5.

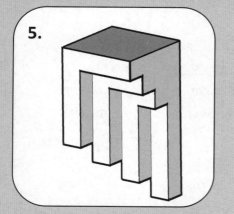

A ▢ D ▢

B ▢ E ▢

C ▢ F ▢

None ▢

6.

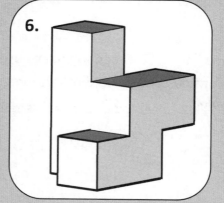

A ▢ D ▢

B ▢ E ▢

C ▢ F ▢

None ▢

Work out which set of blocks can be put together to make the 3D figure on the left.

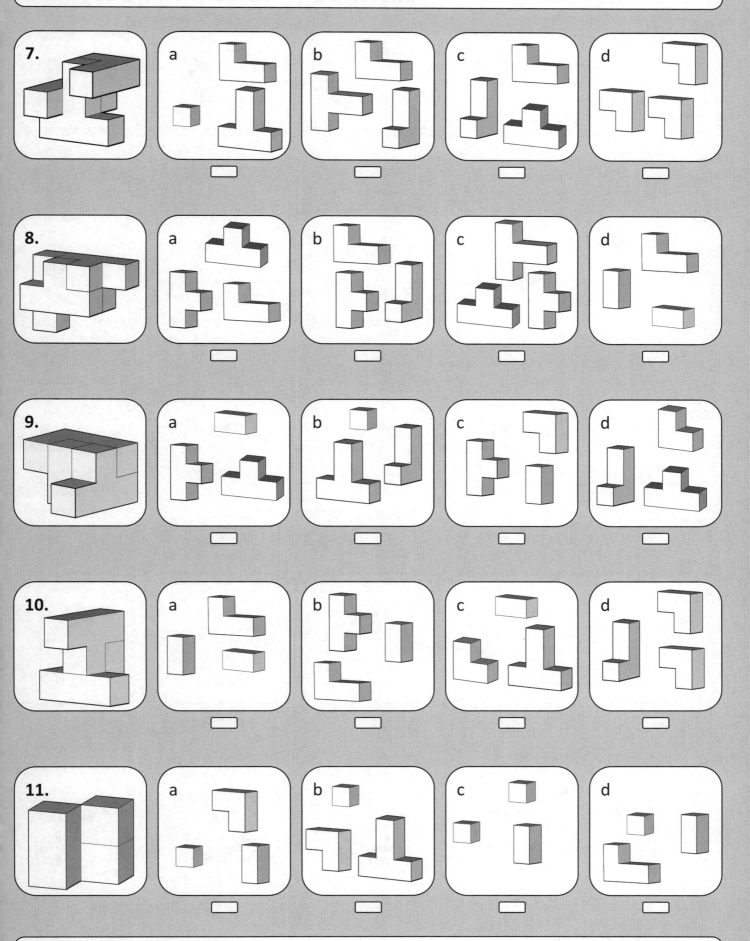

3D Cube Nets

Work out which of the four cubes can be made from the net.

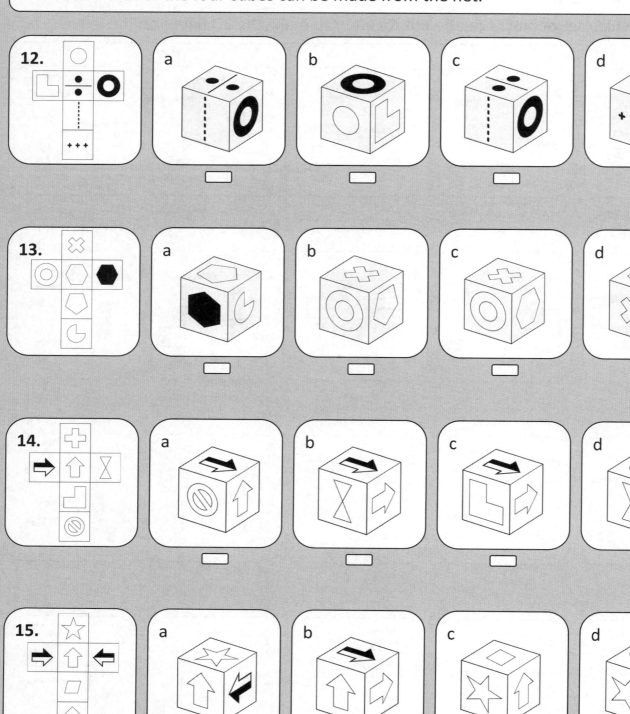

3D Plan Views

Work out which option is a birds eye view (plan view) of the 3D figure on the left.

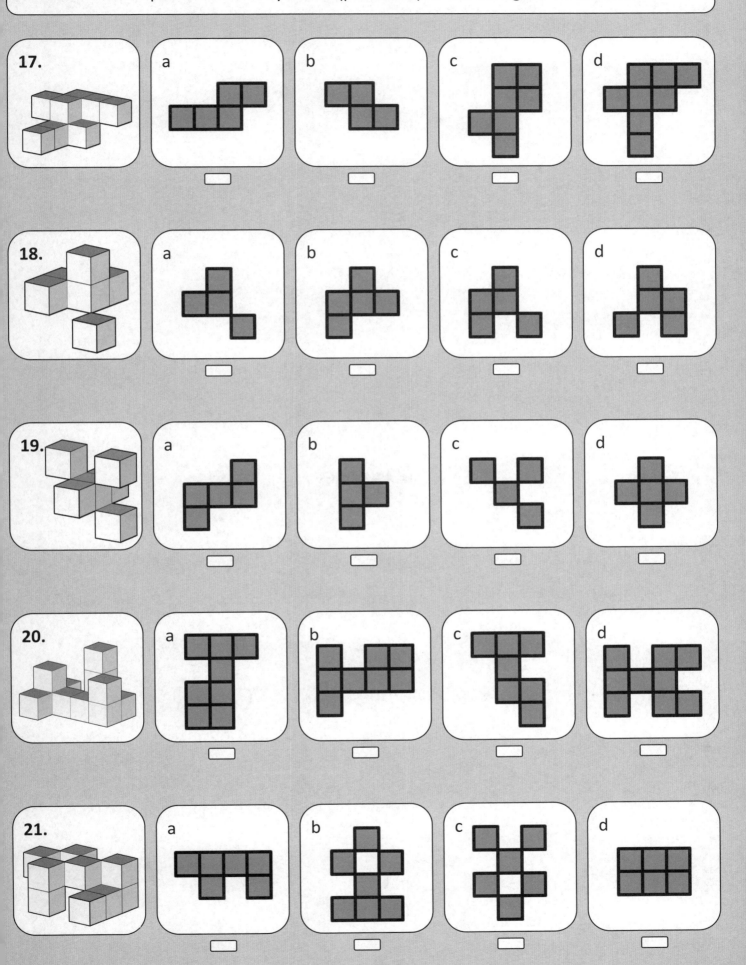

BLANK PAGE

FIRST PAST THE POST® SERIES

3D Non-verbal Reasoning

Answers

As you complete each short test, remember that you can use the 11+ Peer Compare System™ to see how well you performed in comparison to others who have taken this test.

You can register by visiting www.ElevenPlusExams.co.uk/FirstPastThePost to post your results anonymously and obtain the feedback.

Your unique 16 digit access code is:

QYCR-BI08-7Z89-ZVLA

Answers and Explanations

Paper 1 - 3D Views

Page 2		Page 3		Page 4		Page 5	
Question	Answer	Question	Answer	Question	Answer	Question	Answer
1	A	7	C	13	A	19	D
2	D	8	D	14	F	20	None
3	F	9	B	15	F	21	C
4	A	10	F	16	None	22	A
5	B	11	E	17	B	23	C
6	None	12	E	18	E	24	C

Paper 2 - 3D Composite Shapes

Page 8		Page 9		Page 10		Page 11		Page 12	
Question	Answer	Question	Answer	Question	Answer	Question	Answer	Question	Answer
1	c	6	b	11	a	16	b	21	c
2	d	7	a	12	b	17	b	22	a
3	b	8	b	13	d	18	c	23	b
4	c	9	b	14	a	19	a	24	a
5	d	10	d	15	c	20	b		

Paper 3 - 3D Cube Nets

Page 14		Page 15		Page 16		Page 17		Page 18	
Question	Answer	Question	Answer	Question	Answer	Question	Answer	Question	Answer
1	c	6	c	11	b	16	d	21	c
2	b	7	b	12	b	17	b	22	a
3	d	8	a	13	c	18	d	23	d
4	a	9	d	14	a	19	a	24	b
5	c	10	b	15	c	20	c		

Paper 4 - 3D Plan Views

Page 20		Page 21		Page 22		Page 23		Page 24	
Question	Answer	Question	Answer	Question	Answer	Question	Answer	Question	Answer
1	c	6	c	11	c	16	b	21	b
2	b	7	d	12	b	17	c	22	d
3	c	8	b	13	a	18	b	23	b
4	d	9	a	14	a	19	a	24	d
5	b	10	b	15	b	20	b		

Mixed Paper 1

Page 26		Page 27		Page 28		Page 29	
Question	Answer	Question	Answer	Question	Answer	Question	Answer
1	C	7	b	12	c	17	a
2	E	8	c	13	b	18	b
3	None	9	b	14	d	19	b
4	C	10	a	15	b	20	b
5	B	11	b	16	d	21	c
6	E						

Mixed Paper 2

Page 32		Page 33		Page 34		Page 35	
Question	Answer	Question	Answer	Question	Answer	Question	Answer
1	A	7	b	12	a	17	b
2	C	8	c	13	c	18	c
3	E	9	b	14	b	19	a
4	B	10	c	15	a	20	d
5	F	11	d	16	c	21	b
6	D						

Mixed Paper 3

Page 38		Page 39		Page 40		Page 41	
Question	Answer	Question	Answer	Question	Answer	Question	Answer
1	C	7	b	12	b	17	b
2	E	8	b	13	b	18	c
3	F	9	c	14	d	19	d
4	A	10	d	15	c	20	c
5	B	11	a	16	b	21	b
6	D						

Mixed Paper 4

Page 44		Page 45		Page 46		Page 47	
Question	Answer	Question	Answer	Question	Answer	Question	Answer
1	D	7	b	12	c	17	d
2	E	8	c	13	c	18	c
3	C	9	d	14	c	19	d
4	None	10	b	15	d	20	b
5	B	11	c	16	a	21	b
6	A						